4

6

7

SHAKO! THE ESKIMO WORD FOR THE GREAT WHITE BEAR. IT MEANS SIMPLY... KILLER!

SHAKO!

WITHIN THE ARCTIC CIRCLE A U.S. AIRFORCE PLANE, ON A *SECRET MISSION* FOR THE C.I.A., IS IN TROUBLE...

CHARLIE 3 THIS IS HOT DOG! DE-ICERS NOT FUNCTIONING WINGS ICED-UP— *GONNA EJECT!*

IN A U.S. BASE IN ALASKA, C.I.A. CONTROLLER *JAKE K. FALMUTH,* NICKNAMED *"FOUL MOUTH"* BY HIS MEN—

THE HELL YOU'LL EJECT! YOU GOT A *TOP SECRET CAPSULE* ON YOUR WING THAT'S *DYNAMITE* IF IT GETS IN THE *WRONG HANDS!* YOU MAKE A CRASH LANDING— HEAR?

9

BUCK DOLLAR WAS BROUGHT IN...

THE CAPSULE SOUNDS TOO LARGE TO PASS THROUGH SHAKO, BUT WILL REMAIN IN HIS STOMACH, AGGRAVATING HIM. WHAT'S SO *SPECIAL* ABOUT IT?

NONE OF YOUR GODDAM BUSINESS... *DOBIE!* CALL UP ICE STATION DELTA — TELL THEM TO SHOOT THE BEAR IN THE HEAD... AND BRING HIS CARCASS BACK, SO WE CAN RIP OUT THE CAPSULE!

SHAKO HAD, MEANWHILE, LEFT HANK HALF-EATEN. HE WAS ON THE PROWL AGAIN FOR A TASTIER DELICACY... SEALS!

SHAKO CREPT FORWARD...

A SEAL TURNED SUSPICIOUSLY — BUT SHAKO FROZE... HIDING HIS BLACK MUZZLE WITH HIS PAWS, THE WAY HE HAD BEEN TAUGHT AS A CUB...

THEN...

STRUCK!

THE MEN FROM ICE STATION DELTA HEARD THE SEALS BARKING IN PANIC—

OVER THERE!

SHAKO WAS PLAYING WITH THE SEALS BEFORE HE KILLED THEM... LOOK AT THE SIZE OF IT — MUST BE THE ONE WE'RE AFTER!

THE NEXT DAY FOUND SHAKO CHASING A WALRUS OFF THE ICE.

HELL! GETTA LOOK AT THAT BRUTE. IT'S GOT TO BE *SHAKO!* THE BEAR WE'RE LOOKING FOR!

IT'S SHAKO, ALL RIGHT! NO ORDINARY BEAR WOULD ATTACK A WALRUS. BUT WHY MUST WE KILL HIM, FALMUTH? WHAT'S IN THAT *CAPSULE* HE SWALLOWED?

I KEEP TELLIN' YOU, IT'S NONE OF YOUR GODDAM BUSINESS, DOLLAR! JEEZ! IF ONLY THIS FAIRY WAGON HAD GUNS SO I COULD BLOW HIS BRAINS OUT!

SOON THE PLANE LANDED AT ICE STATION DELTA...

HI, FALMUTH, I'M JIMBO JOHNSON, CAPTAIN OF THAT WEATHER SHIP. DON'T USUALLY DO NOTHIN' BUT LAY WEATHER BUOYS, BUT THAT YOGI DONE IN FOUR OF MY MATES!

...SO YOU'RE GONNA HELP US KILL THE STINKER? OKAY, GET ABOARD!

SOON THE SHIP WAS HEADING TOWARDS SHAKO...

CAN'T YOU MAKE THIS OLD TUB GO ANY FASTER, JIMBO? I CAN'T WAIT TO SEE THE BEAR DIE!

SURE, MISTER FALMUTH, SIR! JUST LET ME HAVE ONE MORE - GLUG - SWIG OF THIS BOTTLE!

JIMBO'S REALLY HITTING THE BOTTLE AFTER HIS MATES' DEATHS. WE'RE TAKING A CHANCE SAILING WITH HIM!

WHO'S GONNA HAVE A DROP OF THE HARD STUFF WITH ME?

14

AT THAT MOMENT, SHAKO WAS ABOUT TO TAKE TO THE WATER...

THERE HE IS, CURSE HIM! STUPID BRUTE'S HEADING THIS WAY!

WE CAN'T SHOOT HIM NOW— OR WE LOSE THE *CAPSULE!* I GOT A BETTER IDEA!

WE YANK THE YOGI - HIC - OUT OF THE WATER WITH THIS CHAIN!

OKAY, JIMBO. JUST AS LONG AS WE *DO* GET HIM!

Shako IGNORED THE BOAT. HE WAS THINKING ABOUT THE WALRUS—

IF WE GET BEHIND THE YOGI, WE CAN LASSO HIM. EASY NOW... - HIC!

YAHOOO! WE GOT US A JUMBO FOR... OL' JIMBO!

SNARLING AND SPITTING, SHAKO WAS HAULED UP. SHAKO HADN'T EXPECTED THIS...

SHAKO WAS ANGRY!

Falmuth DREW HIS GUN...

NICE WORK, JIMBO. BUT THE BRUTE'S *MINE!* NOW TO SHOOT IT AND RIP ITS GUTS OUT AND GIT THE CAPSULE!

Suddenly BUCK DOLLAR YELLED...

MOVE, FALMUTH! JIMBO DIDN'T FIX THE CHAIN RIGHT—

IT'S BREAKING UNDER SHAKO'S WEIGHT!

CRACK

NOW IT WAS SHAKO'S TURN. HE WOULD GET **REVENGE** ON THESE RIDICULOUS HUMANS!

SHAKO SEIZED JIMBO...

AAH! THE YOGI'S GOT HIS ≿HIC!≾ TEETH GRINDING INTO MY TOOTSIE!

SHAKO WOULD TAKE HIM AWAY FOR ... **SPECIAL TREATMENT!**

NO, FALMUTH! DON'T SHOOT! YOU COULD HIT JIMBO!

SHAKO SHOOK HIS VICTIM... ENJOYED THE HUMAN'S TERROR...

YOU LOUSY FOOL, DOLLAR! JIMBO'S HAD IT, ANYWAY!

PLEASE... ≿SOB!≾ ...**SCREAM!**

16

SHAKO DRAGGED JIMBO OUT OF SIGHT OF THE SHIP. SUDDENLY HE SPOTTED THE BOTTLE...

YOU WANT A DRINKIE, BOY...? YEAH, HAVE A DRINKIE WITH OL' JIMBO... ⧙HIC!⧘

THE LIQUID WAS STRANGE. WARMER AND SWEETER THAN WATER. BUT SHAKO DECIDED THAT HE LIKED IT!

THAT—THASH A BOY... LEMME TOP YOU UP, YOGI... BEST IRISH WHISKEY ...IT'LL MAKE YOU MORE FRIENDLY...

YOU WOULDN'T EAT OL' JIMBO WOULD YA, YOGI? ⧙HIC!⧘ WE'RE DRINKING PALS NOW..

AS THE DRINK TOOK EFFECT, SHAKO BECAME CONFUSED. HE REMEMBERED ONLY ONE JIMBO—BUT NOW... THERE WERE TWO!

SHAKO WANTED TO HAVE FUN WITH JIMBO—BUT HE COULDN'T LOOK AFTER TWO OF THEM. ONE OF THEM WOULD HAVE TO GO...

CHOKE! NO!

JIMBO'S DEATH CRY! HOW MANY MORE MEN MUST BE TORN APART BEFORE WE GIVE UP, FALMUTH?

AAAAAAAAAAYYYYYYYY!!!

SHUDDUP, DOLLAR! I GOTTA GET THAT SECRET CAPSULE BACK! SO THAT STINKIN' BEAR HAS TO DIE! THIS IS ONLY THE BEGINNING!

FALMUTH PUT A $500 BOUNTY ON SHAKO'S HEAD. BUT THE BEAR WAS A BETTER HUNTER THAN ANY GREEDY HUMAN!

AHHH! ITS HIM!

BACK AT ICE STATION DELTA, **BUCK DOLLAR** HEARD THE MEN'S AGONISED SCREAMS SHAKE THE RADIO...

THAT BEAR NEVER HURT ANYONE 'TILL YOU CAME ALONG, FALMUTH. WHY CAN'T YOU LEAVE HIM IN PEACE?

OKAY, DOLLAR, I S'POSE YOU GOTTA KNOW – BUT THIS IS **TOP SECRET** –

INSIDE THE CAPSULE THAT DARNED BEAR SWALLOWED WAS A **LETHAL NEW VIRUS STRAIN** ... LOOK AT THESE PHOTOS...

"THIS IS A RABBIT BEFORE BEING INJECTED WITH VIRUS... THE OTHER PICTURE SHOWS IT TEN MINUTES LATER – EVERY BONE HAS TURNED TO **JELLY!**"

IT'S THE C.I.A.'S MOST **DEADLY WEAPON** AND IT'S STUCK IN THE BELLY OF THAT LOUSE RIDDEN BEAR!

SO LET'S CUT THE GUFF AND SHIFT YER BUTTS – WE GOTTA GET THAT CAPSULE AND BLOW THE BRUTE'S HEAD OFF!

SHAKO IS THE **FINEST SPECIMEN** I'VE EVER SEEN, AND ALL "FOULMOUTH" WANTS TO DO IS SLASH HIM OPEN. THIS **ANAESTHETIC DART** MIGHT HELP ME SAVE THE BEAR!

LIKE ALL POLAR BEARS, SHAKO WAS EXTREMELY PLAYFUL. HE HAD NIBBLED ONE OF HIS "**PLAYMATES**" AND NOW WAS AMUSING HIMSELF BY ROLLING ON THE OTHER.

THERE THEY ARE! HECK! ONE'S STILL ALIVE.

BLEW ITS LUGHOLE OFF— AND THAT'S JEST FOR STARTERS!

NO, FALMUTH—

MISSED! FOLLOW THAT LOUSY BRUTE.. FASTER! I'M GONNA PUT AN OUNCE O' LEAD INTO ITS ROTTEN BRAIN!

SHAKO TOOK REFUGE UNDER-WATER. HE HAD DONE NOTHING TO THESE PEOPLE AND DID NOT UNDERSTAND WHY THEY HAD STUNG HIM. IT MADE HIM...

ZING!

ZING!

ZING!

OOO MAD!

THE ICE NEAR THE EDGE WAS OVER SIX INCHES THICK. BUT SHAKO'S GREAT BULK SHOT TOWARDS IT LIKE A BATTERING RAM!

AAAAH!

LOOK OUT!

CRASH

WITH ONE SLOG, SHAKO GAVE THE DRIVER A WILD HEAD-ACHE...

CRAC!

NOW HE'S COMING FOR ME..

BUCK DOLLAR'S ESKIMO BLOOD TOLD HIM THAT IF HE RAN HE WAS A DEAD MAN...

MUSTN'T SHOW MY FEAR... THERE'S ONLY ONE CHANCE... ESKIMO TRICK MY PA TAUGHT ME ...GOTTA STARE HIM DOWN!

SHAKO DID NOT FIND DOLLAR INTERESTING. HE NEITHER FLED NOR FOUGHT. THE SIGHT OF BLOOD ON FALMUTH'S FACE ATTRACTED HIM MORE. HE TURNED AWAY...

IT'S WORKING — I'M DISTRACTING HIM... MUST TRY TO REACH MY RIFLE...

AS SHAKO TURNED HIS ATTENTION TO FALMUTH, DOLLAR DIVED ...AND FIRED!

GOTTIM!

YEAH! I RECKON JAKE K. HAS EARNED THE RIGHT TO FINISH THIS BLASTED YOGI — THEN I'LL CUT IT OPEN AND RIP THE CAPSULE OUT!

NO!

SHAKO WANTED TO DEAL WITH THE IMPUDENT HUMAN, BUT HE SUDDENLY FELT STRANGELY SLEEPY...

NICE WORK, ESKIMO. BUT NOW IT'S MY TURN — I'M GONNA DIRTY THE SNOW UP A LITTLE WITH THAT BRUTE'S BRAINS!

ZZZZZZZZ!

THERE'S THE *CAPSULE!* OKAY, COULD YOU AND MR FALMUTH GET SCRUBBED UP? WE'LL NEED YOUR HELP—

WE'LL SHAVE THE UNDERBELLY CLEAN FIRST, THEN MAKE A LARGE INCISION UP THE STOMACH!

WHEN SHAKO OPENED HIS EYES, HE WAS CONFUSED. HE REMEMBERED FIGHTING ON THE ICE... NOW THERE WERE BRIGHT LIGHTS, BLURRED FACES...

SCALPEL!

SHAKO STARTED TO GET UP—BUT HE COULD NOT MOVE. HE TRIED TO ROAR—BUT HIS MOUTH WOULD NOT OPEN...

HEY! THE KNOCKOUT DART'S WEARING OFF! QUICK—GET THE GAS MASK ON HIM!

THAT NOISE—SHAKO *RECOGNISED* THE UNPLEASANT CHAT-TERING OF MEN. *MEN* HAD DONE THIS TO HIM! HE STRUGGLED WITH HIS BONDS...

AAAAH!

THE STRAPS ARE BREAKING!

SHAKO WAS ANGRY!

DID THESE IMPUDENT HUMANS THINK THEY COULD TOY WITH HIM?

FALMUTH'S LOSING A LOT OF BLOOD— GET HIM ON THE TABLE— WE'RE GOING TO HAVE TO OPERATE ON HIM INSTEAD!

UUUH! HE'S TAKEN MY GUN ARM! MY KILLING ARM! I- I'M ONLY HALF A MAN NOW!

SHAKO WAS DISAPPOINTED THAT HE COULD NOT GET BACK IN. HE WOULD HAVE LIKED TO HAVE FINISHED THE HUMANS!

BUT THE PROUD WHITE BEAR HAD WON HIS BATTLE.. AND HE HAD HIS TROPHY!

WE'VE DONE WHAT WE CAN, MR FALMUTH, BUT I'M AFRAID WE CAN'T REPLACE YOUR ARM!

YOU'VE GOT TO TAKE IT EASY NOW, FALMUTH!

NO CHANCE, DOLLAR! WE TRIED IT YOUR WAY— NOW WE DO IT MINE! THE BEAR TOOK MY GUN ARM, SO THIS IS PERSONAL, SEE? EITHER IT DIES... OR I DO!

PERHAPS ONE DAY HE WOULD GET A CHANCE TO EAT THE REST OF THE MAN ...

SHAKO II *THE SEARCH FOR SHAKO* BEGINS ON PAGE 43!

24

JUDGE DREDD ON THE WATERFRONT

MEGA-CITY DOCKLANDS. NIGHT.

A MAN MOVES **FURTIVELY** THROUGH THE TANGLE OF WARESHEDS...HUGGING THE SHADOWS...

...SKIRTING THE POOLS OF BLUE-TINGED LIGHT.

SCRIPT GROVER
ART GIBSON
LETTERING FRAME

UNAWARE THAT HE IS BEING **WATCHED**.

25

DREDD TO DOCK DIVISION — ILLEGAL DICE GAME IN PROGRESS, WHARF 17.

CONTINUING PURSUIT.

FURTHER ON, A SWARTHY MAN WAITS —

CONTACT.

SUSPECT LEM RUDDI HAS MET WITH A CREWMAN OF THE BRAZILIAN VESSEL DOLORES DEL PECK.

THAT MUST BE THE SHIP THAT BROUGHT THE STUFF IN.

SUSPECT'S SAMPLING THE GOODS NOW.

THEY'RE SHAKING HANDS. WE HAVE A DEAL.

YOU WANT US TO SLAP A BUST ON THE *DEL PECK*, DREDD?

NO. WE WAIT UNTIL THE *RUDDI* MOB COME TO PICK UP THE ILLEGALS. THAT WAY WE GET BOTH THE SMUGGLERS AND THE BUYERS.

LEM RUDDI AND HIS PUSHERS HAVE GOT TO BE DRIVEN FROM OUR STREETS — LIKE THE POISON THEY PEDDLE!

*A*N HOUR LATER, FOUR TRUCKS ARRIVE AT THE DOCK GATES —

YOU'RE CLEARED TO ENTER.

LOAD YOUR CARGO AND MOVE OUT! LINGERING IS AN OFFENCE!

ON THEIR WAY, DREDD. GOT DOCKETS TO LOAD FOUR CONTAINERS FROM THE *DEL PECK*.

RUDDI'S IN THE LEAD TRUCK.

*D*REDD WATCHES — WAITS...

*L*ETTING THEM LOAD THEIR ILLEGAL CARGO... GIVING THEM ENOUGH ROPE TO HANG THEMSELVES...

THE THIRD TRUCK HAS CRASHED, BUT THE LAST ONE'S GETTING AWAY!

GATE! YOU GOT ONE RUNAWAY COMING THROUGH!

LOCK THE GATES!

KEEP GOING! WE'LL BUST RIGHT THROUGH THEM!

VROOOM!

SKRANNNGG!

NOW **THAT'S** WHAT I **CALL** A **GATE**!

THE SMUGGLERS ABOARD THE **DOLORES DEL PECK** ARE ROUNDED UP —

AND THE CONTENTS OF THE CONTAINERS EXAMINED —

IT'S THE REAL STUFF, ALL RIGHT. 100 TONNES OF IT — WORTH **BILLIONS** ON THE STREETS!

LOOK AT THIS, DREDD —

— THREE KINDS OF BEANS!

ENOUGH **COFFEE** TO GIVE EVERY ADDICT IN THE CITY A THREE WEEK CAFFEINE BINGE. **SICKENING!**

BURN IT!

THE HEADY AROMA OF ROASTING COFFEE FILLS THE STALE DOCKLAND AIR—

RESPIRATORS DOWN!

OWING TO THE HIGH NUMBER OF POTENTIALLY HARMFUL AND ADDICTIVE SUBSTANCES CONTAINED WITHIN IT, **COFFEE** HAS BEEN **BANNED** IN MEGA-CITY ONE FOR OVER FIFTY YEARS. ONLY SYNTHETIC SUBSTITUTES ARE PERMITTED.

WE'VE WIPED OUT ONE NEST OF PUSHERS—BUT THERE'LL BE OTHERS.

BE SURE OF IT...

...THERE'S A MILLION WOULD-BE **ADDICTS** IN OUR STREETS. AND GRUD KNOWS—

—THERE'S AN AWFUL LOT OF COFFEE IN BRAZIL.

cha cha cha!

ROGUE TROOPER
QUIZ SPECIAL!

Answer these questions about 2000 AD's fighting legend — and prove yourself a Milli-Com Mastermind!

1. Name the two bodylooters who pursued Rogue across Nu Earth.
2. What made Nu Earth such a valuable prize for the Norts and Southers?
3. Which Nort agent used the 'Gentle Touch' to incapacitate Rogue?
4. Name the Nort legion which took part in the Quartz Zone Massacre.
5. Which of Rogue's biochipped buddies was the first to die in the massacre?
6. What was the name of the military satellite to which Rogue tracked the Traitor General?
7. Name the Souther major who returned to Nu Earth to kill Rogue.
8. Which band of Nort & Souther deserters did Rogue once join?
9. How long can a biochip survive outside its energised slot?
10. What special power did Gunnar possess after being re-gened?
11. Name the Genetic Infantrywoman left behind by Helm on Milli-Com.
12. By what other name are Rogue's biochips known?
13. Identify the Chief-of-Staff on Milli-Com.
14. Which piece of Rogue's equipment can use a 'Sammy'?
15. What was the name of the virus which prevented Rogue's biochips from being re-gened successfully?
16. Who was the Souther colonel who secretly employed Rogue?
17. In which zone of Nu Earth did Rogue Trooper first encounter the toxin that could render him helpless?
18. Was Fort Neuro occupied by the Norts or the Southers?
19. How long did Rogue's search for the Traitor General last?
20. To which planet did Rogue travel after leaving Nu Earth?

YOUR RATING:

15-20: Take charge of Milli-Com now! You know all there is to know about future war!
10-14: Brush up your survival tactics and you'll be in the running for a top post in Milli-Com.
0-09: Not a bad attempt, but you'll need to improve your knowledge before you can graduate from your present job as a G.I.'s test-tube cleaner!

Answers

Award yourself one point for each correct answer

1. Bland and Brass. 2. Its location next to a black hole. 3. Sister Sledge. 4. The Kashan legion. 5. Gunnar. 6. Buzzard 3. 7. Magnam. 8. The Marauders. 9. 60 seconds. 10. Telekinesis. 11. Venus Bluegenes. 12. Dog Chips. 13. Nukrom Lamal. 14. Gunnar. 15. The Neva. 16. Colonel Kovert. 17. Polar Zone. 18. The Southers. 19. Three years. 20. Horst.

ARMS BUYER'S ALMANAC

DIARY OF A MAD CITIZEN

January 19th 2107

Something very peculiar happened today.

I rose slightly earlier than usual, to catch the Kenny Kark Morning Spectacular on my holo-vid before venturing out on my weekly jaunt across city to Orinoko's. I'm not really very fond of Kenny Kark — to be frank, he makes me sick — but watching his show every week adds to my sense of occasion. It helps me make my Thursdays special.

I compounded the feeling of celebration by having an extra bowl of Tokyo Joe's Synthi-Soy Soyflakes. "Not a single natural ingredient" it says on the packet. I seem to remember my mother telling me that when she was a kid they had real soy soyflakes. She...

But I don't want to talk about my mother now. I don't want to talk about Kenny Kark, either, except to note that his last guest was a fat lady who'd had her face biosculptured into that of a goldfish. I reckon she has star quality, and if betting wasn't illegal I'd bet my kneepad she makes it big before the end of February.

On second thoughts, I wouldn't bet my kneepad. I mean, I still think the fatty'll strike it rich — but my kneepad's far too precious for me to risk it on the fortunes of fishface. Not precious in a financial sense, you understand — it's just a plain black number with faded diamante GOG lettering, and although it's 17-years-old now it wouldn't fetch more than a couple of hundred credits on the Classique Pad Market. But it's worth a lot more to me; me and that pad have seen 17 years of life together, hard times and worse times. And like they say on the BrainTape Ads: "The tapes cost a 100 — but memories are priceless." How true (although I've seen BrainTapes discounted to 59.50 on the Block Mall).

As the Kark Show ended, I pondered my next move. The journey from my apartment door to the lift is without doubt the most dangerous part of my weekly odyssey. That's not to say the rest of the trip is without its dangers — the Uptown/Downtown Zoom Underpass Pedway, for instance, was voted Top Muggers' Haunt in a recent phone-in, and the crumbling chem-pools along the Reclam Zone are always claiming innocent victims. However, it is a Justice Dept. statistical fact that 50% of all criminal violence is inflicted either within the victim's home, or between his home and his Block Exit.

When I tell you that I live in the Gary Coleman Block, you'll understand my apprehension. Gary Coleman Juves are reputed to be amongst the nastiest, foulest and toughest in the city. I sometimes wonder if they're waging some kind of vendetta or holy war against me, so numerous have the incidents become. But I suppose it makes statistical sense: there are 58,000 people living in Gary Coleman, and it stands to reason that some of them are going to be pestered more than others. And when you consider that dozens of families never leave their apartments, that must lower the odds even more in favour of any particular individual being chosen as a target.

I peered out through my door's Exterior Viewer. The corridor appeared to be empty. A good omen. I unlocked and unbarred the door's triple-security locks and slid out into an alien world. The walls are hidden under a constantly-changing sea of graffiti, chief amongst which are various Juve boasts: GC JUVES RULE, SLINKY KILLS TOASTIES, POWER TO THE SUB-TEENS! and the like. Of course, there's a fair smattering of adult slogans, too. It's a funny thing about graffiti — no matter how fast the Block scrubber squads work, they never seem to be able to keep up with the scrawlers' prolific output. And even when Citi-Def post round-the-clock sentries, the graffiti still appears, almost as if it grew there of its own accord. Now, I paused long enough only to record the fact that someone had scrawled NITCHY IS A FINK in large day-shine letters all over the door, then sprinted for the lifts at the end of the corridor.

As if on cue, the first Juves appeared just as I punched the Call button. I'm not afraid of 11-year-olds, of course, not even when there are a dozen or so of them; but all the same, they can be pretty unnerving. They lounged against the block wall, scuffing their Mock Doc aggro boots noisily. Not one of them said a word. They all just stood there, glaring at me.

I ignored them. I'm used to this sort of treatment; everybody in Mega-City One is. Citizens glare and glower at other citizens wherever they happen to be — though not if there's a Judge around, I hasten to add.

The Juves were obviously unhappy that their glares had failed to bug me. An older boy with a blue-painted face lashed out in my direction with a heavy boot — then stopped his kick just before it struck my leg. None of them laughed, though several sneered provocatively.

I pursed my lips and began to whistle beneath my breath. Stay nonchalant, that's the best motto. Don't give these louts an ounce of satisfaction!

"OW!" I gasped as something small and solid struck me sharply on the back of the head.

"You young devils!" I snapped. "Which of you threw

37

that?" None of them moved. They continued to lounge and glare as if I hadn't even spoken. I felt like shaking them by their stupid shoulders, but wisely refrained. Assaulting a minor is a very serious offence. Of course, assaulting a dult is a serious offence, too — but it would be my word against ten of theirs. "OW!" Another missile cracked against my skull. But thankfully, before they all decided to join in, the lift arrived.

It was empty, except for one Juve with a single 30 centimetre-long spike of rigid, plasticated hair. The point of it stabbed my ear painfully as he squeezed by me.

Thankfully they didn't follow me into the lift. I don't think I could have endured their malicious taunts all the way to street level. I breathed a sigh of relief — and it was then I noticed that the STOP button had been depressed for every single floor from mine down. All 88 of them. Evidently the work of my spiky-headed attacker. But why?

I found out at floor 88.

As the doors slid open, I was deluged by a shower of garbage. The perpetrators, of course, were Juves — whether the same ones who'd menaced me upstairs, I couldn't tell. What's the difference? They're all the same, anyway!

I punched the Close button and fended off a final missile as the doors hissed to. It didn't require a genius to figure out that I was going to receive more of this treatment...all the way down to the street.

By the time the lift reached the bottom, I resembled not so much a decent, law-abiding citizen as a walking muck heap, cleverly constructed over a framework of painful bruises. I am not ashamed to say that I was whimpering.

My journey across the city wasn't exactly pleasant, but compared with my descent in the lift it was a doddle. I arrived at Orinoko's Lunchette in Sector 44's Avenue of Polypropylop. I was afraid the waiter wouldn't serve me, I was in such a state; but happily, he recognised me under the filth and bade me entrance with his usual good-natured gusto. Wouldn't surprise me if I was his best customer — after all, I've been coming here every Thursday lunchtime for 17 years now.

I ordered my usual — soypfel strudle and a jug of synthi-caff — and settled down by Orinoko's big front window. Normally I'd scan the faces of the passing crowds with rapt attention, hoping that maybe today...maybe today I'd find the face I'd been looking for all these years.

But the 88 peltings I'd received at the hands of those surly, sinister Juves had entirely spoiled my mood. I sat there, a muck-encrusted 40-year-old with a heavy heart and no prospects...just another big city loser...a man who couldn't even find his own dear mother...

There, I've said it. Mother's the reason I come here every week. It's in the hope that one day she'll come in here, just like she did every Thursday back in the old days, and say in that lilting, laughing voice of hers: "Mockola for me and a freezipop for the brat." We were happy together, Mom and me; why, when Dad died in the big SpacePort disaster back in '86, we hardly even noticed. Times were hard, but me and Mom were together, and that was always enough for me.

But as I got older, we started to grow further apart. When I finished with my unemployment courses, Mom insisted that I become independent, move out, set up house on my own. I guess she wanted to live her own life, taste a little freedom for a while. But she was my Mom, for Josh-sakes; I couldn't leave her.

So Mom did the next best thing: she left me.

It was a few days after my 23rd birthday. I'd been out on a cheap-shop trip and picked up this great GOG kneepad — yes, the very one I wear to this day. I came rushing into the house, yelling to Mom to look-see the new pad. My voice echoed round an empty home. Mom

had packed her clothes — and everything that wasn't bolted down — and vamoosed.

I was distraught. I asked the neighbours if they knew where she'd gone — most of them didn't even know who she (or I) was. The Judges were neither helpful nor very sympathetic. "Look, pal — we got enough to do fighting crime without busting our guts to find a lady who's "abandoned" a 23-year-old!" as one of them so forcefully put it.

The only hope I had was Orinoko's. Mom used to come here every Thursday after her Principal Fondobics work-out; I'd come over from the apartment to meet her, and she'd tell me about those mysterious exercises she learned.

I checked with her Fondobics instructors, but they were only vexed that Mom had split without paying her overdue tuition fees. So I took to hanging out in Orinoko's at that same time every Thursday, in the faint hope that one day she'd come back. And she never did...

I felt a tear dribble down my cheek, pushing a small heap of muck before it. I didn't even try to wipe it away. What was the point? Insulted and beaten up by Juves; unemployed and unemployable; friendless and alone; a man whose own mother had deserted him. Who cared if I cried or not? Who gave a mutie's curse?

"I do, Pizmo."

The voice was low, throaty — the sort of voice they use to advertise hi-class clinics. A friendly voice. It seemed to come from under the table. I looked down, expecting to see maybe a television set or a lurking dwarf.

"No dwarf, Pizmo," the voice said. "It's me. Your kneepad".

January 20th

I broke off rather abruptly yesterday. I needed time to absorb the implications of that amazing incident. Finding that my kneepad could talk wasn't all that big a deal; I mean, anybody who watches holovision (which is everybody) sees a dozen equally amazing things in their own living rooms every week. A talking kneepad isn't really more surprising than a dame with a goldfish face, or men like the fatties who can eat a tonne of food at one sitting.

No, what amazed me was the fact that my kneepad cared. And even more — it cared about me.

I started to ask it how come it had never told me this before, but the kneepad cut me short. "I can't talk here," it said. "Someone might overhear. Let's go home."

So we did.

Back in my apartment the questions I was bursting to ask came pouring out. "Why did you never speak before? What's your name? Does it hurt when I kneel on you?"

The kneepad ignored them. "For the past 17 years," it began, "I have been studying humanity from the vantage point of your left knee. My studies have now reached an end. I have formulated a conclusion — and from your point of view, Pizmo, a very grim conclusion it is."

A little shiver ran up my spine. "Wh-what is it?"

"Simply this: that you, dear Pizmo, are the victim of a city-wide agreement which has resulted in you becoming a victim for all and sundry to persecute at will."

I could hardly believe my ears. "This is incredible!" I gasped. "It's like you've been reading my mind. I've

often wondered what I did to deserve a life like mine: no job, no prospects, plagued by sinister Juves, a man whose own mother..."

"Yes, yes, Pizmo," the kneepad put in impatiently. "I know all that. The question is — what are you going to do about it?"

I shrugged helplessly. "What can I do? Like you just said — everybody in the city's against me. The only place I might get help is in foreign parts — like Texas City, maybe, or Brit-Cit. But there's probably a conspiracy to stop me leaving town — and besides, I have no money."

"You're too negative, Pizmo," the kneepad told me. "Adopting a more positive attitude would be of immense benefit. Yes, I think that's where we'll start..."

It talked on into the evening. I have a feeling that my life is going to take a sudden turn for the better.

January 21st

On the advice of my kneepad, I have taken up Hari-ip-Slip, the ancient Oriental art of self-defence through Positive Posturing. From a basic ten or so slinky body movements, I am constructing a dancing defence that will leave those Juves speechless.

I had a lengthy chat session with my kneepad — it refuses to be called GOG; evidently that's its designer name, not its own. It made a rather startling suggestion: I might not be the only victim of this sinister conspiracy. There may well be thousands — even millions — of other citizens like me, living in lonely torment, completely unaware of kindred souls nearby.

We also discussed extra-sensory perception. As a result, I am conducting an experiment: for 10 minutes every hour I am focussing my thoughts and beaming them telepathically to the city at large. If there are others like me they will hopefully respond.

January 22nd

Spent today in bed, worn out. I suppose it was the exertions of last night's mental telepathy. My kneepad is hanging on the chair, but it hasn't said a word all day. I suppose that intellectuals are moody, even in the kneepad world.

January 23rd

In complete contrast to yesterday, I feel fantastic! I am convinced that I have had a telepathic reply to my mental messages. When I wakened this morning, in that hazy warm space between dreams and living, I heard a voice say quite distinctly: "I am Mrs Gorp, your next-door neighbour. I am like you." My kneepad got quite excited when I told it. "It figures, it figures," it kept saying. "You see, Pizmo, I've been thinking: it's possible to extend my theory to include everybody in the whole city!"

I knitted my brows. Somehow, that didn't seem scientific to me. But the kneepad rushed on: "I mean — what if every citizen, all 400 million plus of them, is just the same as you. To wit: Lonely, afraid, no job, no future, no money, persecuted by Juves...they wouldn't all have been abandoned by their mothers, of course, but a lot of them might be."

"But if we're all the same, who's behind the conspiracy?" I asked.

"Who do you think?" the kneepad said. "Who's the common factor in all the equations? Who persecutes everybody?"

Like all great truths, it was so simple that I wondered how I hadn't thought of it myself. The Juves. Of course — it was the Juves who were behind everything!

January 24th

We've hatched a plan. We're going to alert the entire city to the conspiracy, but gradually, so as not to tip our hand to the Juves prematurely. I have been delegated to make contact with Mrs Gorp. I left my apartment at noon, after ascertaining that the Juves were nowhere in sight. I puzzled for a moment over NITCHY BAKS BLOO, which someone had scrawled on my door. Some secret Juve code perhaps?

My push on Mrs Gorp's bell was light but confident. Her voice rasped suspiciously from the answer-grille in the doorframe: "Whoozit? Whoddyawant?"

"Pizmo Nitchy, Mrs Gorp. From next door. We met at the Block-fest a couple of years ago." I bent closer to the microphone and lowered my voice. "I got your telepathic message. We have a lot to talk about."

There was a long, long pause. Then a new voice — a man's — blared in my ear: "Lizzen, weirdo! I count ta ten, I open da door. Ya still there I tear off ya legs an' make ya eat 'em!"

"Obviously her husband isn't as advanced as she is," my kneepad hissed. "I suggest we return to base and revise our plans."

My kneepad soon hit on another scheme: "Letters to the vidzines — that's the answer. If we get enough printed, the citizens'll soon get the message. Of course, the Juves might see the letters, too. But that's a chance we'll just have to take."

It was risky, but I consoled myself with the fact that not many Juves can read. Of course, not all that many adults can either. It took me an hour to compose a document setting out my discoveries and theories. including a masterly analysis of my main Juve Conspiracy ideas.

(I had better record here: I am not trying to take credit away from my kneepad when I say "my" discoveries and theories. The kneepad itself insisted that I delete all reference to it throughout, on the grounds that it had no right to disturb the status quo of the kneepad world over what was essentially a human problem. I asked it what it meant.

"If citizens at large found out that your kneepad can talk, they'd want to know why their own kneepads can't."

"Well — why can't they?"

"Oh," said my kneepad, "most can. It's just that they choose not to.")

January 25th

Spent the entire day composing letters to newsvids, vidzlnes and holovid shows, including one to Kenny Kark. My kneepad thinks Kark might be a Juve spy, but I'm not so sure. He's pretty tall for a Juve.

January 26th

Thursday again. Time for my weekly trip to Orinoko's — but the usual fear of going out was absent this morning. As soon as I reached the lift, the Juves arrived on schedule. They launched into their usual glare and sneer tactics — but this time, I glared and sneered right back. I elbowed one of them aside and lounged against the wall, looking as contemptuous as possible. This is all part of the Hari-ip-Slip method. 60% of all Juves will shuffle off if treated like this.

Not a Juve shuffled. I knew that this meant they had accepted my challenge to their challenge, and events were now likely to escalate. No matter. I have surprised even myself with how well I have mastered the martial art.

So when the first Juve aimed a blow at me, I was ready. I swayed back out of his reach, causing him to lose his balance and strike one of his bald associates on the head. The bald Juve snarled — and hauled a cosh from a pocket in his zipporak.

All hell broke loose. I ducked the cosh with a Snaking Weave, combining it with a sideways Dragon Slide that took me out of range of the fists that tried to smash me from behind. A Juve closed in from each side, one wearing studded Knocknux, the other swinging a short stave. I did a double Dodge-Duck on the spot, and the stave hit the knux kid full in the mouth.

That's when I made my mistake. I should have executed a Backward Long Slither and worked myself away from them. Unfortunately, I paused long enough to titter about the Juve who'd been hit.

It was my undoing.

A dozen hands grasped at me, pulling me down. A hard, bald head cannoned into my stomach, winding me. I tried to summon up the strength for a desperate Leaping Leopard — but it was too late. I was submerged in a sea of boots and fists and swinging sticks...I don't know how a Juve gang decides when its victim has had enough. I'm glad they do, though. As suddenly as it had begun, the whole melee was over. The Juves disappeared along the corridors, and I was left to pick myself up, rubbing my wounds, feeling dazed and a little sick.

"You... okay, kneepad?" I looked down. Horror of Horrors! My kneepad — my mentor — my saviour — was gone.

It must have been ripped off in the struggle, and the Juves had carried it off — no doubt to torture and interrogate. Despair spread through my veins like ice water. It was all over. Without my kneepad, I was nothing. It had been my only friend — had kept me sane and relatively cheerful through this black time. I would never see it alive again.

Dejected, dispirited, I slouched back into my apartment. The scrawl on my door had been changed to NITCHY BOKS GREE, presumably during the fracas, but I didn't pay it a second thought. I knew in my heart there was only one way out of it for me now...

I opened my living room window and clambered up onto the ledge. It was a long way down to the ground: 89 storeys. Nobody could possibly survive that drop. I took a deep breath, closed my eyes and prepared to jump...

"Hold it, citizen!"

I whirled, to see the impressive figure of a Judge framed in the living room doorway. "Attempted suicide is a serious offence." He took a step towards me, but I waved him back. "I'm sorry, Judge. I've never broken the Law before, but I...I just can't go on. Without my kneepad to tell me what to do, there just doesn't seem any point. I've no-one to talk to me any more."

"Hold on a second." The Judge spoke quietly into his wrist-communicator, then a voice blared up from the street far below.

"Pizmo!" it cried. "Pizmo!"

I leaned out a little and, fighting the dizziness, looked down. On the street far below I could make out the shapes of a few Justice Dept. vehicles, and the tiny figures of some Judges.

"This is your kneepad, Pizmo!" the tinny voice went on. "Don't jump! I'm safe! The Judges found me. Come on down and claim me back!"

I turned back to look at the Judge in my doorway. "That doesn't sound like my kneepad," I told him.

"It's speaking through a megaphone, Pizmo" the Judge replied. "Makes 'em all sound a bit funny." He stepped further into the room, and stretched out a gloved hand. "Come on in now. I'll take you to your pad."

There were tears in my eyes as I allowed him to take my hand and lead me out to the lifts.

January 29th

Of course, it was a trick. They hadn't really found my kneepad at all. It was another Judge hollering through the loudspeaker. They were very nice to me, though, if a trifle brisk. They brought me here, to this Justice Dept. Psychiatric Cube, where XXXXXXXXXXXXXX XXXXXXXXXXXCENSORED BY ORDER OF CHIEF JUDGE MCGRUDER XXXXXXXXXXXXXXXXXXXXX

February 9th

I'm cured now, the medics tell me. I can go home soon. They've been encouraging me to keep up my diary. They say it makes a splendid hobby, and a good hobby is more than half the battle against the possibility of further bouts of Future Shock. So I think I will stick at it.

I watched the Kenny Kark Spectacular this morning on the Cube holo. Funny how Kenny doesn't seem to be half as nauseous as he used to. If gambling wasn't illegal I'd have won that bet, too — the goldfish woman was his star guest. She's evidently Number One in the Musi-charts with a thing called Ant Egg Salad.

February 10th

I've decided I won't bother going to Orinoko's any more, looking for Mom. The Judges traced her for me — she married an alien and moved back to Alpha Centauri with him. So I don't suppose she'll be coming to the Mega-City for her Thursday lunchettes. Perhaps she'll write to me.

Looking back, all that stuff with the kneepad seems like a dream, like it all happened to some other Pizmo Nitchy, not me. I mean, kneepads don't have any vocal cords, so how could it speak? (They don't have brains either, so it couldn't have been communicating telepathically.) And how could a kneepad know all about things like Juve conspiracies? It never told me that. Still, I can't help remembering something my kneepad said — or rather, I can't help remembering something I imagined my kneepad said: "Most kneepads can talk. It's just that they choose not to."

I wonder why?

TEXT: ALAN GRANT ART: ERIC BRADBURY

THE END

DURING THE LONG NIGHT OF ARCTIC WINTER, DRIVEN BY THE URGE TO MIGRATE, THE TINY RAT-LIKE CREATURES CALLED LEMMINGS RUSH IN A SINGLE LINE TO PLUNGE STRAIGHT INTO THE SEA—

SHAKO! II

BIOLOGISTS HAVE NOT BEEN ABLE TO UNRAVEL THE MYSTERY OF THE LEMMINGS' MASS SUICIDE—

BUT SHAKO WAS NOT CONCERNED BY MYSTERIES. HE WAS CONCERNED WITH EATING! AND THE LEMMINGS WERE WILLING FOOD.

THE CREATURES WERE A TASTY SNACK—THEY SEEMED TO FALL RIGHT INTO HIS MOUTH!

AND LATELY HE DID NOT FEEL LIKE FIGHTING FOR HIS FOOD AT ALL...HIS STOMACH OFTEN HURT HIM...

43

WEEKS EARLIER SHAKO HAD SWALLOWED A CAPSULE CONTAINING A DEADLY TOP-SECRET VIRUS WHICH WAS STUCK IN HIS STOMACH

BUT THERE WERE THOSE WHO WERE DESPERATELY *HUNTING SHAKO!* EARLIER THAT DAY A U.S. ARMY DOG TEAM HAD SET OUT FROM THE SPOT WHERE SHAKO HAD KILLED THE OILMEN... ON BOARD, CIA AGENT *JAKE K. FALMUTH* — AND HIS SIDEKICK, *DOBIE.*

WE GOT THAT WHITE BRUTE'S SCENT — AN' *THIS* TIME HE *AIN'T* GETTING AWAY!

DRIVING THE SLED, HALF-ESKIMO ECOLOGIST, BUCK DOLLAR —

EVER SINCE THE BEAR BIT HIS ARM OFF, FALMUTH'S BEEN CRAZY FOR *REVENGE*... BUT WE'RE IN INTERNATIONAL TERRITORY HERE. AN' IF THAT CAPSULE FELL INTO *ENEMY* HANDS — IT WOULD CAUSE A *WORLD-WIDE DISASTER!*

SOON...

THE ANIMALS ARE GOING WILD — THEY HAVE THE BEAR'S SCENT, AND HE'S CLOSE.

YEAH — GETTIN' SO'S I CAN ALMOST SMELL HIM MYSELF! O.K. DOBIE — *LET 'EM LOOSE!*

SHAKO WAS ALERT WHEN HE HEARD THE FIRST HOWLS. WARILY, HE FACED THE ONCOMING PACK...

NEXT SECOND THEY WERE ON SHAKO. *BITING* HIM. *TEARING* AT HIM!

OTHER ANIMALS WOULD HAVE FELT FEAR—FEAR OF *DYING!*

BUT SHAKO KNEW ONLY FEAR OF *LOSING!* IT MADE HIM FIGHT ALL THE STRONGER...

DARN THAT BEAR! DOGS ALL OVER HIM—AND *STILL* THEY CAN'T *LICK* HIM!

DON'T SHOOT, YA *LAME BRAIN!* HE'S MOVIN' TOO FAST. HIT THAT CAPSULE IN HIS STOMACH AN' HALF AMERICA WILL DIE! *INCLUDING US!*

I'LL PLUG HIM FOR YA, CHIEF!

BUT TWO OF THE DOGS HAD BEEN TRAINED TO HUNT BEAR... THEY CAME IN SLOWLY, WIDE APART...

SUDDENLY, YELLOW FANGS SUNK INTO SHAKO'S REAR!

THEY KEEP BITIN' HIS BACKSIDE AN' BACKIN' OFF SO HE HAS TO **SIT DOWN** TO PROTECT HIMSELF. COME ON, LET'S GET DOWN THERE—

SHAKO WAS TRAPPED. THE WILY DOGS KEPT JUST OUT OF REACH OF HIS SWEEPING CLAWS...

KEEP YA FINGER OFF THAT TRIGGER DOBIE—THIS IS ONE JOB I'M GONNA DO MYSELF!

I'VE BEEN WAITING A **LONG TIME** FOR THIS, YA LUMP OF **CATMEAT**—AND NOW I'LL BLOW A HOLE THROUGH YA HEAD SO WIDE I'LL BE ABLE TO DRIVE A **TRUCK** THROUGH IT!

TWO SHOTS RANG OUT...

BANG BANG

AND TWO DOGS DIED INSTANTLY! SHAKO COULD NOT UNDERSTAND—HE THOUGHT THE MEN WERE GOING TO SHOOT HIM!

DROP THAT GUN, AMERICAN, OR WE **CUT YOU DOWN!**

IVANS!

RUSSIAN SNOW TROOPS. THEY MUST'VE FOUND OUT ABOUT THE VIRUS CAPSULE! THEM ON ONE SIDE, US ON THE OTHER AND THE BEAR IN THE MIDDLE. THERE SURE IS GONNA BE **BIG** TROUBLE!

48

BUT FIRST THERE WAS THAT ENTICING SMELL OF WHALE BLUBBER TO INVESTIGATE.

HE HAD NEVER SEEN SO MUCH FOOD IN ONE LUMP—ENOUGH TO FEED A POLAR BEAR FOR MANY SEASONS!

SHAKO ONLY WANTED A SNACK. THIS PUNY HUMAN SHOULD NOT HAVE INTERFERED...

IT'S KNOCKED URI INTO THE BLUBBER SHUTE!

SHAKO COULD NOT RESIST DIVING AT A RICH SLICE OF BLUBBER...

STAVA! IT'S THAT KGB MAN'S BEAR—

AAAGGHH

AAAGGH!

THE—THE BOILING VATS—NIET! NIET!

THE KGB MAN RACED ON DECK...

MY MEN HAVE HIM CORNERED—NO THANKS TO YOU. I WARNED YOU THAT BEAR WOULD BE TROUBLE!

ALL IN A GOOD CAUSE. NOW STAND ASIDE, COMRADE CAPTAIN—

IN THE BOWELS OF THE FACTORY SHIP, NICOLAI BOSNAVICH DANOVICH WAS STILL SEARCHING...

COUNTDOWN TO
THE APOCALYPSE WAR

YOU BUTTON PUSHERS ARE GONNA TASTE SOME ACTION!

"Let the Apocalypse Begin!"

With these four, short words, Supreme Judge Josef Bulgarin unleashed the might of East-Meg One's military forces upon an unprepared Mega-City.

The nuclear conflict that followed was described in 2000 AD Progs 245-270. At its end, the twenty-five instalment story had run to one hundred and fifty-three pages of missiles and mania, and been read by five hundred thousand Earthlets.

These were not the only people, though, to don their rad cloaks and seek shelter from the rain of East-Meg missiles.

Since 1981 the adventures of Judge Dredd have also appeared in the Daily Star newspaper. Mostly, these adventures have been original stories, but some have retold famous events in Mega-City One. The Apocalypse War became one such event to earn a repeat showing when it appeared in the Daily Star on Saturday, 18th September, 1982.

However, because the Star strips run to only half a page in length, the Apocalypse War had to be drastically shortened...to eleven pictures!

That eleven picture "remix" is reprinted overleaf, along with the five subsequent Star strips that described the events after the war as Mega-City One struggled to return to some form of normalcy. (Though life in the future city could never be properly described as normal!)

So, for those veterans who read the Apocalypse War during Progs 245-270 — it's time to take cover once again. The countdown begins now!

10..9..8..7..6..5..4..3..2..1..KLIK!!

CRIMINAL ERROR

JUDGE DREDD

THE PERP'S SUFFERING IS *OVER*. IN THE CITY OF THE FUTURE, WHEN ONE LIFE IS WEIGHED AGAINST 400 MILLION, THE LAW HAS THE *FINAL WORD*!

KWABLLAAM!

HOWEVER, I AM PERMITTED TO OFFER YOU AN ALTERNATIVE.

PLEASE! PLEASE... *DO IT*!

YOU CANNOT BE PERMITTED TO CARRY **CONTAMINATION** BACK INTO THE CITY!

IT AIN'T... FAIR! I COMMITTED... A CRIME! YOU'VE GOTTA **ARREST**... ME! IT'S MY... **RIGHT**!

JUDGE DREDD... HELP ME!

THERE'S NO HELP FOR YOU. MY **CLOAK** PROTECTS ME AGAINST THE RADIATION — BUT YOU'VE RECEIVED A **LETHAL DOSE**.

FEEL **SICK**! FACE IS **BURNIN'**!... GOTTA GET OUT OF HERE —

UP AHEAD —

SURVIVAL PROCEDURES OBSERVED. RAD-CLOAK AND ANTI-RADIATION PILLS.

MEGA-CITY ONE, 22ND CENTURY. **JUDGE DREDD** PURSUES A FLEEING PERP —

PERP ENTERING **RESTRICTED ZONE**! **JUDGE DREDD** PURSUES A AM **PURSUING**!

DANGER RADIATED ZONE

EEEEE — EAGH!

JUDGE DREDD

DANGER UX NUKE

THE EVACUATION COMPLETE, JUSTICE DEPARTMENT *BOMB SQUADS* MOVE IN —

NO WAY WE'RE GOING TO DEFUSE THIS ONE WHERE IT IS. WE'LL HAVE TO LIFT IT OUT AND DETONATE IT AWAY FROM THE CITY.

THUNKKK!

OH, WELL, BACK TO THE DRAWING BOARD.

OKAY, OKAY, WE'RE *LEAVING!*

DROKK!

EASY DOES IT — *EASY, I SAID....!*

NOT TO MENTION *SECTOR 403.*

SO MUCH FOR COOLIHAN.

SECTOR 403 HAD TAKEN THE FIRST *NUCLEAR STRIKE* OF THE *APOCALYPSE WAR.* NOW, A MASSIVE DECONTAMINATION AND RECLAMATION PROGRAMME WAS WELL UNDER WAY —

JUDGES BEGIN A HASTY EVACUATION —

IT AIN'T FAIR, JUDGE DREDD — WE JUST MOVED BACK IN!

WE'VE HAD ENOUGH OF BEING PUSHED AROUND! WE'RE *NOT LEAVING!*

DEMOLITION CREW TWELVE TO SITE CONTROL...WE'VE FOUND AN *UNEXPLODED WARHEAD.*

IT'LL BE TRICKY. JUDGE COOLIHAN'S GOING TO *RIDE* IT OUT, TRY TO STOP ANY SUDDEN JOLTS.

START WHEN YOU'RE READY. GOOD LUCK!

JUDGE DREDD
THE WALL GAME

LATER, DREDD SPEAKS TO THE CHIEF JUDGE.

THE REFUGEE PROBLEM IS TYING UP TOO MANY JUDGES.

BUT WHAT CAN WE DO? THESE PEOPLE ARE STARVING...

NOTHING WILL STOP THEM TRYING TO GET IN!

FIVE MORE FOR THE HOLDING PEN. LOCK 'EM UP TILL MORNING, THEN SEND 'EM BACK WHERE THEY CAME FROM.

DON'T WORRY — THIS JOB'S SO BIG IT'LL LAST AND LAST!

BUILDING A WALL TO KEEP OURSELVES OUT! TRUST DREDD!

AND SO —

REBUILD THE WALL!

BUT THE LURE OF THE CITY IS TOO GREAT FOR THE STARVING REFUGEES. BY NIGHT, THOUSANDS TRY TO ENTER ILLEGALLY THROUGH GAPS IN THE SHATTERED CITY WALL —

HOLD IT! YOU'RE UNDER ARREST!

THE FOLLOWING DAY, DREDD'S PLAN COMES INTO OPERATION —

THE CITY IS WILLING TO MAKE ONE CONCESSION! WE OFFER YOU FOOD — IN RETURN FOR WORK.

TERRIFIC! WHAT DO YOU WANT US TO DO?

CORRECTION — EX-CITIZENS! YOU FORSOOK ALL RIGHTS WHEN YOU ABANDONED YOUR CITY TO THE INVADERS!

I THINK I MAY HAVE THE SOLUTION.

DURING THE APOCALYPSE WAR, MILLIONS OF CITIZENS HAD FLED MEGA-CITY ONE FOR THE DUBIOUS SAFETY OF THE CURSED EARTH. NOW THEY WANTED TO RETURN.

WE'VE TOO MANY DISPLACED PERSONS WITHOUT ADDING TO THE PROBLEM! THERE'S NO ROOM FOR YOU!

YOU CAN'T DO THIS TO US! WE'RE CITIZENS OF MEGA-CITY ONE!

THE MUTIES FROM MILTON KEYNES!

After the atomic war of 2150, New Britain became a divided nation.

Where once there had been harmony, prejudice ruled. For the war had produced a terrible side-effect. Strontium 90, present in the nuclear fallout, had warped sections of the populace, making them easy targets for those lucky enough to have escaped the mutating effects of the radioactive isotope.

In 2167, the mutants rebelled. Led by General Armz, and his second-in-command Johnny Alpha, the mutant army fought a bitter battle with the ruling forces.

At the war's end, the mutants had won themselves the right to live in peace, albeit only in specially designated mutant areas.

Every major city had one, but the largest was in Milton Keynes. Within the ramshackle ghetto, the Muties of Milton Keynes struggled to make some kind of life out of their squalid existence. But they needed money to improve their environment, and so it was that the Milton Keynes Mutants' Association began saving every credit they could scrape together.

But it soon became clear that they could never amass enough money on their own, and so they decided to risk all they had by sending their best gambler to Vega, the huge gaming resort orbiting the Earth at two hundred miles up.

The M.K.M.A.'s top cardster was Nobby Clarke, aptly named because of the lumps that covered his entire face.

With him went Billy Glum and Snivel Hurst. They knew that if Nobby played his cards right he could win enough money to modernise the ghetto, build decent homes and schools.

On arrival on Vega, the three mutants headed for Fat Jax's. Nobby Clarke justified the faith held in him by winning a cool four hundred thousand credits — enough to realise all their dreams. But tragedy struck when the joyous threesome were attacked by Fat Jax's men and robbed of their winnings. Nobby Clarke and Snivel Hurst both died in the the attack, but help was at hand for Billy Glum. He was rescued by Johnny Alpha, who was taking time off from his job as a bounty hunter — one of the few jobs a mutant could get.

Alpha not only gave over his winnings to Glum, he also made sure that Fat Jax never crooked anyone again. For when Jax accused Johnny of cheating and drew a blaster, Johnny shot first and Fat Jax died at his own, crooked table.

Ten years were to pass before Johnny Alpha and Billy Glum met up again, but this time Alpha was working... and his assignment was to track down a fellow mutant hiding out somewhere in New Britain.

Now, for the first time, the story of that chance re-acquaintance can be told. It begins on the page opposite...and ends in the death of one of Johnny's own kind.

UND STERNHAMMER STREET! VULF IS *FAMOUS* TOO!

STERNHAMMER STREET

THE MILTON KEYNES *MUTANTS' ASSOCIATION*— THIS IS WHERE MY CONTACT USED TO WORK.

MILTON KEYNES MUTANTS' ASSOCIATION

*O*NCE, JOHNNY AND WULF HAD DONE THE MUTANTS OF MILTON KEYNES A BIG FAVOUR. SEE 2000 *A.D. PROG* 189.

HALLO, BILLY.

JOHNNY! JOHNNY ALPHA! THIS *IS* AN HONOUR!

MAYBE YOU WON'T THINK IT'S SUCH AN *HONOUR* WHEN I TELL YOU *WHY* I'M HERE.

BEAST BOLSOVER— KNOW HIM?

UH...UH, N-NO, JOHNNY!

*J*OHNNY'S MUTANT ALPHA EYES EMIT PIERCING *ALPHA RAYS* — RAYS THAT CAN STRIP A MAN'S MIND BARE!

PLEASE, JOHNNY! DON'T ASK ME TO NORM ON BEAST!

YOU'RE LYING, BILLY. HE'S HIDING HERE. *WHERE?*

WHY NOT? AFRAID OF HIM?

BEAST? **HECK, NO!** HE WOULDN'T HURT A **FLY!**

WARRANT SAYS **MURDER**, BILLY.

BEAST NEVER DID IT!

THEN HE'S NOTHING TO WORRY ABOUT! HE'LL GET A FAIR TRIAL.

FAIR TRIAL? ON COLONY 3? THEY **HATE** MUTIES THERE, JOHNNY! ALL BEAST'LL GET IS A **LYNCHING!**

I'LL MAKE YOU A **DEAL.** YOU TAKE ME TO BEAST AND I'LL HEAR HIM OUT. IF I **LIKE** WHAT I HEAR — WELL, WE'LL SEE.

YOU MEAN IT? **THANKS**, JOHNNY!

BILLY GLUM GUIDES THEM THROUGH THE MAZE OF TWISTING, DECREPIT STREETS — —

THAT STRONTY DOG — IT'S **JOHNNY ALPHA!**

THE FAT ONE'S STERNHAMMER — THE ONLY **GOOD** NORM I EVER HEARD OF!

THEY'RE COMING THIS WAY! IT'S YOU THEY'RE AFTER, BEAST!

WHAT'M I GONNA DO, AUNT MA? THEY'LL **S-SHOOT** ME!

GET OUT THE BACK WAY — ME AN' YOUR UNCLE PA WILL HOLD THEM OFF!

THAT'S THE HOUSE — —

THERE HE GOES!

STOP RIGHT THERE, MR. ALPHA!

YOU TAKE ANOTHER STEP AN' SO HELP ME, WE'LL *SHOOT*!

YOU'RE MAKING A MISTAKE, MR. BOLSOVER. JOHNNY ONLY WANTS TO *TALK* TO BEAST!

NO! THIS GHETTO OWES YOU A LOT, MR. ALPHA — AND WE'RE GRATEFUL FOR IT...

BUT OUR BEAST'S *INNOCENT!* WE'LL NOT STAND BY AND LET YOU GUN HIM DOWN.

DAMN RIGHT, MRS. B! WE'RE WITH YOU!

THIS GOES ON MUCH LONGER, SOMEBODY'LL GET *HURT!*

SPDFFFFF!

≶COUGH!≶

≶HACK!≶

HE VENT THAT VAY!

WHAT THE HELL--?

69

THEN IT WAS SHAKO'S TURN. HE WANTED ONE-TUSK ON ICE...

HEY— GET A LOAD OF THAT!

UP ABOVE A SPOTTER PLANE CIRCLED...

HE'S PULLIN' THAT WALRUS OUT OF THE WATER— THAT'S ONE BIG BRUIN!

COULD BE THE BEAR WE'RE AFTER. GET A MESSAGE OFF TO THAT C.I.A. GUY, FALMUTH!

SHAKO IGNORED THE PLANE. HE WAS INTENT ON THE KILL...

JUST GIVE ME ONE MORE CHANCE, SIR!

MEANWHILE, AT ANCHORAGE U.S. BASE, ALASKA, JAKE K. FALMUTH WAS RECEIVING A DRESSING-DOWN FROM HIS SUPERIOR IN THE C.I.A. ...

YOU GOTTA ADMIT, CHIEF, YOU'VE SURE BEEN ACTING FUNNY SINCE SHAKO BIT YOUR ARM OFF!

LET'S GET THIS STRAIGHT, JAKE. A BEAR SWALLOWS A CAPSULE CONTAINING OUR DEADLY COLD WEATHER VIRUS. NOT ONLY DO YOU FAIL TO KILL THE BEAR, YOU ALMOST START THE THIRD WORLD WAR BY ATTACKING A RUSKIE SHIP!

OKAY, JAKE. BUT YOU MESS IT UP AGAIN AND I'LL PERSONALLY SEE YOU END YOUR DAYS AS COFFEE BOY IN OUR BOLIVIAN OFFICE!

HURRIED PREPARATIONS WERE MADE AS SOON AS THE SPOTTER PLANE'S REPORT CAME IN...

YOU MESS THIS UP, CHIEF— THEN I'LL GET YOUR JOB. HOPE THERE WON'T BE ANY HARD FEELINGS— I MEAN, YOU'LL WRITE ME FROM BOLIVIA?

SHUT YOUR MOUTH, DOBIE. WE'LL HEAD OFF TO WHERE THAT PLANE SIGHTED THE BEAR...

SOON, FALMUTH, DOBIE AND OTHER C.I.A. MEN WERE BEING CARRIED ALONG THE ALASKAN COAST...

SHAKO'S TRAIL LED TO A TRAPPER'S LODGE...

U S
ARMY

YESSIR, THAT BEAR WAS HERE 'BOUT AN HOUR AGO...GOT SO ANGRY 'COS HE COULDN'T GET AT ME, HE TOOK IT ALL OUT ON MY SMOKING HUT!

THAT'S SHAKO, ALL RIGHT. HE'S REAL MEAN! BUT WE GOT HIM THIS TIME!

BEST TO HOLE UP HERE TILL IT BLOWS OVER. YOU WON'T LOSE ANY TIME - SHAKO WILL HAVE TO FIND SHELTER, TOO!

WON'T FIND HIM IN THIS BLIZZARD, MR FALMUTH!

THE HELL I WILL!

U.S. ARMY

GET IN THE SNOW-CAT, PACKER. WE'RE GOING HUNTIN'!...

SHAKO WAS NOT FAR AWAY. HE HAD TAKEN SHELTER IN A CAVE ON A SNOW RIDGE, BUT THE SOUND OF THE SNOW-CAT BROUGHT HIM OUT TO INVESTIGATE.

77

DOWN BELOW—

OKAY, DAMMIT! THERE'S BOUND TO BE A CAVE UP THERE IN THAT RIDGE!

SHAKO WAS ASTONISHED TO SEE THE TWO MEN RUNNING TOWARDS HIS OWN CAVE. HE THOUGHT THESE HUMANS MUST BE VERY STUPID.

SNOW'S COVERING THE BEAR'S TRACKS, MR FALMUTH. WE'VE GOTTA FIND SHELTER BEFORE THIS STORM GETS MUCH WORSE!

YOU TAKE FIRST GUARD, PACKER!

SURE, THOUGH I DON'T SEE WHAT THERE IS TO GUARD AGAINST. DON'T RECKON WE'LL BE SEEING THAT BEAR AGAIN!

AAAAH! FALMUTH, HELP ME!

H-HOLY SMOKE IT'S HIM!

HE'S BRINGING HIM INTO THE CAVE!

FALMUTH...

78

SHAKO WAS PLEASED WITH HIS CATCH. THE MEN WERE LARGE AND FLESHY.

HE-HE'S PUT ME DOWN. WH-WHAT THE HECK'S HE PLAYING AT?

SHAKO SETTLED DOWN TO WAIT. THE BLIZZARD COULD LAST A LONG TIME—IT WAS GOOD TO HAVE A STORE OF FRESH, WARM MEAT.

I GUESS HE AIN'T HUNGRY JUST YET. GOTTA FIND SOME WAY OF GETTIN' TO THAT RIFLE!

AS LONG AS THAT BEAR IS SITTIN' THERE, WE AIN'T GETTING NOWHERE. WE'RE JUST ONE BIG HUMAN PANTRY!

BACK AT THE TRAPPER'S CABIN, FALMUTH'S MEN WAITED ANXIOUSLY. 12 HOURS PASSED, 24 HOURS...

A DAY AND A HALF, AND NO SIGN OF FALMUTH. WHEN IS THIS STORM GONNA LET UP, DOLLAR?

I'VE KNOWN THEM LAST THREE WEEKS!

WHEN SHAKO AWOKE HE WAS FEELING HUNGRY. HE DECIDED HE'D EAT ONE OF THE MEN.

THE BRUTE'S GONNA MAKE A MEAL OF ONE OF US. YOU'RE JUNIOR, PACKER—YOU GO FIRST!

YOU-YOU CAN'T ORDER ME TO BE EATEN!

I'LL MAKE IT EASY PACKER—THIS'LL DEADEN THE PAIN!

UUUGH!

79

82

SHAKO COULD NOT GET THE BARB OUT. ANGRILY HE TURNED ON DOLLAR.

I–I AIMED FOR THE **HEART**, BUT HE'S **STILL STANDING**...

AAAAGH!

WHEN DOLLAR DID NOT RETURN, THE LIEUTENANT INVESTIGATED...

DON'T YOU WORRY, DOLLAR BOY. WE'LL GET YOU TO HOSPITAL!

NO...I'M DYING ANYWAY. MIGHT AS WELL...STAY HERE, SET A TRAP...

I...I HURT HIM BAD. HE'S GONE OFF...THEN HE'LL BE—BE BACK TO FINISH ME OFF...

LISTEN...WANT YOU TO DIG...A HOLE SO HE CAN'T COME...COME AT ME FROM BEHIND...BURY ME **ALIVE**!

SHAKO HAD GONE TO THE ICE EDGE TO BATHE HIS WOUND...

AN ICY GUST OF WIND REMINDED HIM IT WAS TIME TO MOVE SOUTH AGAIN. BUT FIRST...

...FIRST HE WOULD **FINISH OFF** THE HUMAN.

BURIED UNDER THE RUBBISH WAS BUCK DOLLAR—

IF I'M GOING TO DIE—SHAKO IS GOING TO COME WITH ME!

JUDGE DEATH

THE WINNER

JUDGE DEATH

This hideous being from another dimension can kill with just one touch of his claw-like hands. Standard gunfire has no effect on his cadaverous body and incineration serves only to release his evil spirit. In this form, Judge Death can possess others and continue to carry out his aim of destroying all life.

For, on his world, it was decided that since all crime was committed by the living, then the living should die — sentenced by Judge Death and his fellow judges.

Accompanied by three of these killers, Judge Death crossed over into our own dimension when all life on his world had been extinguished.

Though defeated in all his attempts to successfully inflict his warped justice on the living, Judge Death remains a fearsome foe. Should he ever return, life will not be worth living!

INTELLECT: 8   RUTHLESSNESS: 10
STRENGTH: 9   INVINCIBILITY: 10

DANGER·RATING:

THE MEKON

This green-skinned Venusian is a cold and calculating strategist whose goal is the complete control of the Universe.

The Mekon's power lies in his awesome intelligence, which he uses to gain domination over others. He has an army of Venusian warriors called Treens who carry out his bidding without question. With few exceptions, their loyalty is absolute and they are willing accomplices to his evil.

Other than his supreme intelligence, the Mekon has no other natural powers. In contrast to his mind, his body is frail and weak. Without his ingenious "flying-chair" he is defenceless.

Though he has suffered defeat several times, the Mekon remains a threat to Earth. Should his quest for galactic domination ever succeed, a new dark age will dawn on free worlds everywhere.

INTELLECT:	10	RUTHLESSNESS:	9
STRENGTH:	1	INVINCIBILITY:	3

DANGER·RATING:

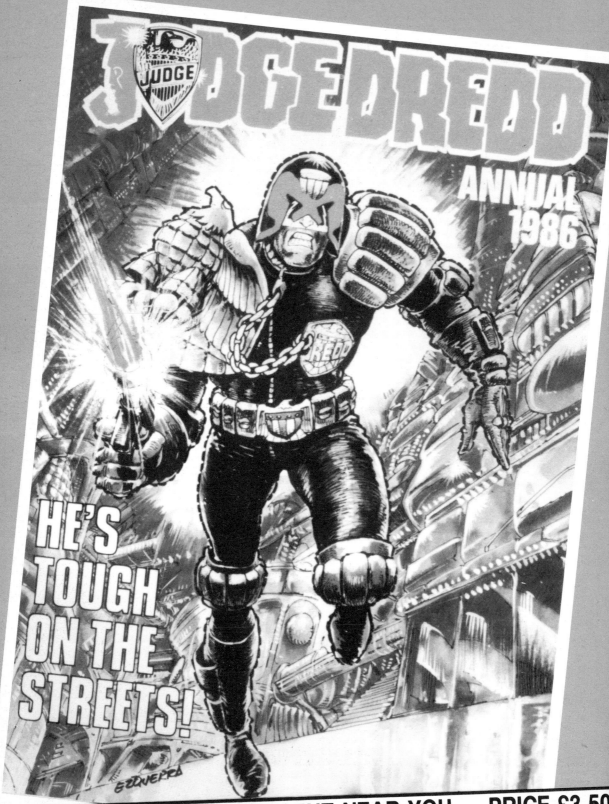

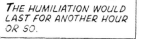

BAKABAKKA

HE'S GOT A HOVEM— AAGH!

THE FOOL DOESN'T STAND A CHANCE— THAT THING WON'T TAKE HIM MORE THAN A HUNDRED METRES!

THEN WE'VE GOT HIM WHERE WE WANT HIM...

FUN HOUSE

GET THOSE CANNON UP HERE! MOVE IT!

I DON'T DESERVE MERCY... NOT AFTER MY AWFUL CRIMES!

P-PLEASE! I'M BEGGING YOU... MERC----

BLAAM!

WHADOOM!

94